Renovation Reference Guide

Understanding the Language of

Construction

Presented By

Wooton Construction

www.homeprojectcenter.com

Notice

Construction is an ever-changing field. Standard safety precautions must be followed, but as new research, changes in technology, tools, and materials become available, changes in procedures and language may become necessary or appropriate. Readers are encouraged or advised to check the most current product information provided by the manufacturer of tools and products for proper usage and methods. Readers should also always verify any construction language or procedure information with current and localized information through the appropriate jurisdiction for their project. Neither the publisher nor author assumes any liability for any injury and/or damage to persons or property arising from this publication.

.

Table of Contents

Introduction

The following Manual contains essential information about construction tasks that are performed during any Renovation project. The intent is to give anyone taking on a project the ability to quickly reference terminology needed. Included are tips at the end of each Category to help further assist in a project. Some suggestions are a part of regular home maintenance.

Included are Industry terms as well as those specifically related to a Task Category of construction. By formatting the terms by subject matter, it makes it easier to find.

For the novice, I have included a section on calculating your measurements. Using these formulas will help in purchasing materials for your Project.

Most importantly, Safety First! Even if you have taken on projects before, it is always good to brush up on Safety skills. Construction is an area that even the most seasoned Tradesman can be injured if he is careless or not mindful, especially while operating power tools, climbing ladders, or not using their materials correctly.

Commonly Used Industry Terms

General Contractor – has extensive knowledge of construction building and its process. Generally, he does not perform work personally but hires the individual Tradesman and teams to perform the specific tasks. He makes the work schedules, and Tradesman providing oversite and quality control inspections of the work being performed for the entire Project.

Sub-Contractor – commonly referred to as a Sub. The specialized Tradesman hired to perform work on a project. An example would be Foundation work, Masonry (*brickwork*), Painter, Finish Carpenter, etc.

Square Footage – the area measurement in feet. Length in feet x Width in feet = Square Footage. It is used to figure flooring, drywall space, ceiling space, the tile needed for floors, shower walls, niches (indented box in shower wall to store shampoo and soap bottles), general living area, countertops, backsplashes.

Linear Footage – this is the unit measurement of any material in increments of 12 inches = one linear foot. It is used to measure trim: crown, baseboard, shoe molding, door trim, window trim, siding trim, fascia, etc.

Squares – this is a common term used in roofing to notate the amount of roofing needed. Each Square represents 100 square feet.

Floorplan - this is a 2D drawing denoting all exterior walls, interior walls, doors, openings, windows, cabinetry, plumbing items (*tub, showers, toilets, sinks, washers*), electrical items (*lights, fans, outlets, switches, meters, etc.*) with unit measurement annotations in feet and inches. Floorplans are made using a scaled measurement. The most common are 1/8" =1', ¼" = 1', or ½" = 1'. This will be noted on the drawing on the lower left- or right-hand corner.

Layout – used in Building and/or Design plans showing the placement of walls, doors, cabinetry, plumbing, and electrical items to scale. Floorplans help significantly in creating the Design of a home, being able to see the space and flow of the space.

Elevation – This is the visual drawing of a 3D object from the object's front or sides—usually, the house's sides, cabinets, or the wall's framing.

Scope – in construction, this refers to the line itemize description of work to be done by Task Category

Raw Materials – These materials are used to build a home. They are necessary yet have no design element to them. Example: stick lumber, fasteners, sealants, mud for Drywall, waterproofing materials in tile work, etc.

Finish Materials – also known as Design Materials. These materials are essential in their look as well as their function. These materials will finish the look or overall Design of the Project. Example: faucets, light fixtures, tile, flooring, trim, cabinet styles, hardware, etc.

Sourcing – this is the process of finding a needed or desired material, determining the manufacturer, distributor, pricing, and how to get it shipped or delivered.

Backer Materials – these materials are Raw Materials needed to adhere to other Finish materials. They provide structural integrity as well as waterproofing. Example: concrete board and waterproofing behind tile shower walls, the thin-set under tile, plywood, and house wrap under or behind the siding, etc.

Plumb – perfectly vertical.

Level – perfectly horizontal

True - staying in as straight of a line as possible but making allowances for unevenness or imperfections. Usually used when lining up new construction with existing out of level or plumb construction

Spec Sheets – The Specification Sheets for any product that needs to be installed, such as a faucet, light fixture, or appliance. It will have exact measurements of the manufacturer's product and recommendations on the proper way to install it. The Spec Sheet should include the list of appropriate tools needed to install the product.

Site Plan – this is a plan for the Job Site (*where the construction is done*) that will involve workstations, clean-out stations, storage areas, delivery, and drop off locations.

CODES – this is a part of the City Development and Planning Commission in any city that oversees the construction projects in the area. They uphold and maintain Construction Standards & Practices to ensure that the construction is a minimum standard of construction deemed sound and safe. This department will assist in construction for any building, commercial and residential, from beginning to end. For Residential projects, they are to be involved when adding living space to existing structures or making any structural changes to the existing building.

Cut-off or Waste: a term used to indicate the percentage of materials that will either be "wasted" or no good because it is the cut-off end piece of wood, tile, pipe, etc. it cannot be used for anything else and is considered to be an acceptable waste. Each Project has it. Most framing materials, flooring materials, and siding materials are shown with a 10% overage to accommodate this.

Calculating Materials

You will need to determine the quantities you need for each material you need and/or have selected. The three most common measurements to calculate are as follows:

Length – is the longest measurement of a given room.

Width – is the shortest measurement of a given room

Square Footage –(ft²) **total square footage = length in feet x width in feet**.

Reading a tape measure

Before calculating any measurements, it will be necessary to know how to read a tape measure. Most tape measures have lines denoting a specific measurement. Each line is a "tick" on the tape. Every inch will have 16 ticks, each one equals 1/16th of an inch. Larger lines mark ¼ or ½ inch notations.
Note: Some tape measures have each "tick" noted. However many of these have standard and metric measurements. Be aware of what you are buying.

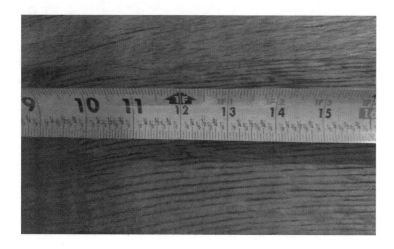

Wall Square Footage

Wall Square Footage

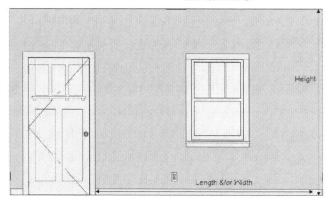

Linear Footage = this is the total length in feet. Often used when referring to the total length of cabintry and trim.

Count – the number of items needed. The most common things you will use this for are the following:

> Windows & doors, hardware
> Soffit Vents
> Lights: cans, Heat/Light/Vent, Light/Vent, outlet & switches
> Tile Trim pieces
> Thresholds

Roofing: Squares – this is a common term used in roofing to notate the amount of roofing needed. Each Square represents 100 square feet. Example: 1200 square feet = 12 squares

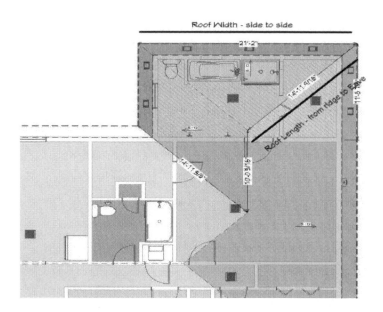

Calculating the Square Footage of a roof for Asphalt Shingles or Torch Down roofing:

Sqft = (ft²) length *(from the ridge to the eave of a roof)* in feet x the width *(side to side of a single roof plane)* in feet. You will have to calculate that for each roof plane (side of roofing) and add them all together to have the Total Square Footage

<u>Metal Roofing</u>: metal roofing panels sold are in 16″ – 24″ panels; you will have to know how many panels to buy.

16″ wide: **(the width of roof x 12 ÷16) + length of roof = total linear footage needed**.

<u>Framing: you can</u> calculate the amount of stick framing needed, although time-consuming.

<u>Studs</u>: if your studs are 16″ on center - **length of the wall x 12 ÷16 = the number of studs**

Add in 2 more studs for each corner, window, and door framing.

<u>Rafters</u>: If your rafters are 24″ on center – **width of the Roof ÷ two = the number of rafters**

Add all roof planes together for your total. *if rafters are 16″ on center, use the formula above.

<u>Plywood</u>: walls – since plywood installed is vertical, the length of the wall ÷ 4 = sheets of plywood.

Roof – since the plywood is installed horizontally (the width of roofline ÷ 8) + (length of the roof plane ÷ 4) = plywood sheets. You will have to add up all roof planes to get your total.

Siding:

<u>Brick</u>: square Footage needed x 5.5 = the number of bricks to order. You will need overage just in case of breakage and cut off. So, multiply to total by 10% for your total amount of bricks to order.

<u>Lap siding</u>: depending on the size of the lap siding you are getting, each board sold is a specific length and width. Check the amount of square Footage the board covers. Example: 8″ wide lap siding at 12 foot long will cover about 7 sqft. The manufacturer will usually indicate the coverage. You will calculate the square footage needed **by the wall's length x the wall's height = the sqft**.

Stucco: **the length of the wall x the height of the wall = the sqft**.

Insulation: _walls_ – the length of the wall x the height of the wall = the sqft needed. Add all walls together.
        Ceiling: the width of the room x the width of the room = the sqft.

Drywall: _walls_ – the length of the wall x the height of the wall = the sqft needed. Add all walls together.
        Ceiling: the width of the room x the width of the room = the sqft.

Flooring: the width of the room x the length of the room = the sqft. When ordering flooring, always add 10% to the total square footage for waste and cut off.

Tile: _walls_ – the length of the wall x the height of the wall = the sqft needed. Add all walls together
        Floors: the width of the room x the width of the room = the sqft. When ordering tile, always add 10% to the total square footage for waste and cut off.

Countertops: the length of the base cabinet x the base cabinet's depth = the sqft of materials needed.

Trim Work: base crown, shoe molding, casings, etc. are measured by total length.

Cabinetry is measured by the total length filling the space and individually by the cabinets' size needed to fill every space depending on the cabinet's use.

Architectural Blueprint Symbols: Symbols utilized in standard building and construction drawings. Being familiar with these symbols will help when communicating with a builder or architect abou

Architectural Blueprint Symbols

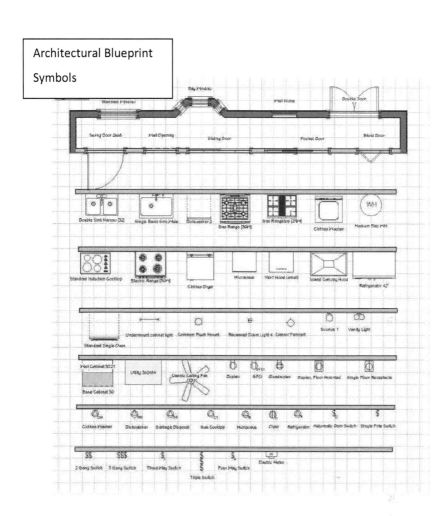

Task Categories & Definitions

The following terminology is for the Task Categories of Construction. While each Category involves many different and specific Tasks, they are the main Categories of work involved in any Renovation and/or Building Project. Each of the following Tasks listed below is in the order of the Construction Process.

Demo – This is the removal of building materials.

Foundation – the base on which a structure is built.

Framing – the construction of the structure; walls, ceilings, roof, windows & doors

Roofing – the construction of the top of any structure to give protection from weather and temperature changes.

Siding – the outer cladding of any structure

Insulation – the method of helping protect the interior space from outside elements of moisture and temperature

HVAC – Heating, Ventilation and Air Conditioning

Plumbing - the installation of drain and supply lines for water and gas fixtures

Electrical – is the installation of electrical cords and boxes to give power supply to the structure.

Drywall – the interior wall coverings to give protection, insulation, and fire safety for the structure.

Painting / Staining – this is the color coating added to walls (*interior and exterior*), trim, doors, ceilings, etc.

Tile Work – this is the installation of tile to walls, floors, etc.

Flooring – this is the installation of any material to cover the foundation of the structure.

Cabinetry - cabinets are the storage boxes used in kitchens, baths, utility rooms, and storage rooms in many styles to suit many purposes.

Countertops – this is the top to the base cabinets giving working space.

Finish Carpentry / Trim Carpentry – the installation of the finishing touch to any construction project. Example: any molding pieces, bath accessories, hardware, etc.

Product Schedules - this is a chart of a Design Finish product and/or which will denote the location, quantity, size, style, color, and any needs notes relating to the product. The following products will need a Schedule written out: Paint, Windows, Doors, Plumbing Fixtures, Electrical Fixtures, Tile & Cabinets. The following is an *EXAMPLE* of those schedules.

Paint			
Area	Color	Base	Sheen
Kitchen walls	SW 7015 repose Grey	Latex	Eggshell
Kitchen trim	SW 7004 Snowbound	Oil-based	Semi-gloss
Tile	Color	Size	Grout color
Kitchen backsplash	Bright white	3x6	Platinum grey
Kitchen Flooring	Blue Slate	12x24	Steel Blue
Windows	Color	Size	Style
Kitchen	White vinyl	3030	4 lite standard

-

Safety First

In the Construction Industry, from the Tradesman to the Homeowner, the most important thing to know and practice is Safety First! Significant to Minor injuries will likely happen due to carelessness and a lack of awareness, a lack of attention in the surroundings, knowledge of the materials used, and lack of ability to use tools properly. Even an experienced Tradesman can get injured if they are distracted, careless, and/or try to misuse a tool or equipment. Severe injuries will cost time, money, and even lives. The following are the most basic and essential guidelines to know about construction safety.

The Basics: knowing the tasks, tools, equipment, and materials used and how to use them properly is essential. A good rule to follow is if you do not know how to perform a Task, then DO NOT do it!

Cease Fire: if there is anything on a job site that looks even remotely dangerous, everyone has a right to call a "ceasefire" to get everyone to stop what they are doing to prevent an accident from happening. Never be afraid to shout out if you see a situation that looks like it may result in an injury. Better safe than sorry.

Tasks: if you have never performed any construction tasks before, it is best to be instructed by an experienced Tradesman for that specific Task. EXAMPLE: If you do not have an understanding of how properly execute electrical work and wiring, then you run the risk of burning your house down, causing significant injury to yourself, and putting those around you in danger as well. This rule applies to any Construction task from Demolition to Clean-up.

Protective gear is a must.
   Gloves are worn for better grip as well as minor injury prevention.

Safety glasses and goggles when cutting any material from wood, stone, tile, glass, etc. will protect your eyes and parts of your face from injury.

Hard-Hats are worn on most sites in the construction of the framework to protect the head from materials and/or tools from hitting the head during use.

Harnesses are worn when working on high scaffolding, ladders, and/or rooftops to prevent someone from falling straight to the ground resulting in Major injury or even death.

Masks are worn to keep dust and debris out of your mouth and nose. It will also prevent mold, allergens, and other harmful substances from being inhaled.

Back braces are worn when lifting any materials to protect the back.

Steel-toe Boots (shoes) help prevent injury to your feet if materials and/or tools if dropped.

Tools: before using power tools, there must be proper training on how to use it.

Nail guns that use air compression will have a safety feature on the tool that should be engaged when the gun is not being actively used to prevent the nail gun's accidental firing. The nails coming out of the gun can injure a person like a bullet with the amount of air compression used. Also, when attaching and removing the air hose from the nail gun, use caution. Keeping the gun and hose away from the face and body as possible and a firm grip on both will nail will help prevent the gun or hose from flying back into the body, causing injury. *Saws* should always have a guard on the saw: Circular saws, a Sawzall, Table saw, Jigsaw, Routers, Multi tools, etc. For the handheld power saws, always make sure your materials are stable. Through the use of work tables (*which may consist of a sheet of thick plywood and sawhorses*), vice grips (*when needed to hold a piece of wood securely*), and always make sure to work at a comfortable height and angle. If the height and angle used for cutting are awkward, then there is a risk of making a bad cut and/or injuring injury.

Handheld Tools are to be gripped tightly when in use. They should always be stored away to ensure they are not stepped on or tripped over while moving around the job site. Handheld tools will serve a specific purpose. EXAMPLE: do not use a flat head screwdriver as a hammer. Misuse of the tool will make the Task take longer and result in injury to the hands.

Equipment used on a job site to help reach high areas, lift, or move materials and/or people can cause serious injury if not used properly. Training is required to use this equipment.

Mechanical equipment such as excavators, forklifts, platform lifts, etc. requires experienced operator training. If you have no training, do NOT attempt to use the equipment.

Ladders & Scaffolding: Do NOT overextend the reach on a ladder or scaffolding. There are markings on a ladder to indicate the highest rung (*or step*) considered safe to stand on while in use. This marking is so that a person's balance is not lost and prevents falls from the ladder resulting in major and minor injuries.

Assist equipment: such as dollies, wheelbarrows, etc. do require caution. Do NOT overload a wheelbarrow with debris or material. Misuse will result in damaging the wheelbarrow, dropping needed materials, and/or injury. When using any equipment intended to move large amounts and/or heavy materials, always scope out a path first and ensure that path is clear of any tools, equipment, materials, and debris. Ensure anyone in the immediate area knows that large and/or heavy materials are being moved so they will not get in the way.

Materials used on a job site require safety measures in their use, handling, and storage.

Use & Purpose: Always use the right materials for the right Task. Using material for something it is not intended for will ruin the build's integrity and a breakdown later. EXAMPLE: when framing a large opening longer than 4-foot-wide, a 2x4 piece of lumber is used, then eventually the opening will sag and may result in damaging the Drywall, trim work, and paint. The 2x4 lumber is not meant to hold the weight of the span. A larger piece of lumber, such as a 2x6, should be used in the framing.

Material Storage: when setting materials down, always use caution not to damage the material. It is never thrown or dropped down. It is always placed down. A place should always be chosen before moving the materials. It is better to move it once than multiple times. It should be placed out of the work area, pathways, and weather.

Handling: flammable and combustible liquids should never be stored in any environment that is over 100 degrees. The fumes should never be inhaled, come in contact with skin or eyes. Wear protective eyewear when using these materials. Always read the warning and use labels and follow the manufacturer's instructions.

Lifting: knowing the proper way to lift materials and equipment is essential to prevent bodily injury. Back braces should be used when doing any lifting to protect the back. When bending down to pick up a tile, bags of grout or cement, lumber, etc. always bend your knees when going down and lift with your legs. Keep your arms slightly bent at the elbows to prevent hyperextension and ensure a better grip. If you have a hard time standing up with the material in your hands, it is too heavy. Get help moving it, either from another person (*especially lumber, plywood, and* *drywall sheets*) or use a dolly. Getting help will prevent back injuries as well as injury to the hands and feet. When assisting someone is moving or handling materials, and you are not familiar with how heavy it may be, test it out by lifting the material on edge to gauge the weight. You will feel it. Never twist your body while lifting and/or carrying materials.

Site Cleanliness: keeping a job site clean is essential. A job site should be cleaned throughout the day and at the end of every day.

> *Debris* and food items left out will cause tripping hazards, which will result in injury.
>
> *Equipment and tools* are correctly picked up and stored will prevent anyone from stepping on them and damaging themselves or the tools and equipment.
>
> *Keep Cords & Hoses* out of walking paths, water and not set on or under other equipment or materials. Check all electrical cords should be checked for proper connection into power sources. Never use electrical cords that have exposed wiring; this can result in injury.

Earphones (earbuds): the volume on headphones, earbuds, etc. should be kept at a volume that allows you to hear the other workers around you and the tools being used. A coworker, Homeowner, or Vendor dropping off materials may need your help or need to give you instruction and/or warning that you will need to hear. If the music is too loud, it will result in not being aware of the surroundings. If you can not hear, it will lead to backing into equipment, materials, and/or people, causing a fall or dropping of tools and materials.

Spotters: having someone with you when performing dangerous tasks such as high work on roofs, scaffolding, and ladder or any electrical work, can save a life. Always have some assist you with heavy lifts and moving around materials.

Demolition Terminology

Demolition - (**Demo**) removing any structural member, appliance, Fixture, building material, foundation. There are different levels of Demolition from partial to the full gut. It cannot be stressed enough for all Demolition the importance of gloves, hats, eye protection, and breathing masks. These will help prevent injuries sustained from wood and other stone materials from flying in your face, falling on your head and protect your lungs from breathing in the dust from these materials removed from the home.

Equipment:

- Trash trailers – may be a rental or owned, on wheels with a hitch to move from to job and taken to the Landfill. If the Vendor owns, will need to bring to the Landfill to empty. You will **not** be able to throw out mattresses or couches with foam cushions. Paint cans will have to be empty and in black contractor bags. You will need to check with the Vendor to find out what items are acceptable to throw away. Some materials, such as lots of concrete, will need specific equipment. Other materials such as landscaping, carpet, mattresses will require certain landfills to be disposed of properly.

- Dumpsters: - most dumpsters are rentals. Not on wheels, will require a removal and drop off service. There are different types of dumpsters: landscaping, concrete, building structure.

- Excavators: a large machine with a large, toothed bucket on end to be able to dig into the soil and debris piles to scoop up debris and dump into the dumpster. They can be used to move large piles of soil and level off the ground to ready for foundation and/or future drainage or landscaping.

- Ditch witch is a large machine used to dig trenches for drainage or bury pipes, conduits, etc.

- <u>Tampers</u> – used to pack soil to make dense and firm for foundations or pools.

- <u>Augers</u> – machines used to dig large and small holes that need to go deep. An example would be for footings, posts, etc.

- <u>Genie lift</u> – is a machine that is used to lift workers into very high places.

- <u>Scaffolding</u> is a ladder and platform system to reach high places, allowing the Tradesman to walk back and forth to work.

- <u>Floor strippers</u> – machines used to scrape the glue and/or mortar from a concrete slab.

Tips & Standards:

1. Demolition Standard: in all Demolition, it is crucial to wear proper safety glasses, gloves, breathing masks, and NO loose clothing or jewelry that may get caught on nails, boards, or equipment!

2. To ensure all nails, screws, staples, and all fasteners are removed from studs, take a roll of painter's tape and/ or a scrap board of wood and run over the studs from the top wall plate down to the bottom wall plate.

3. *Clothes washers* - tuck the drain hose into the tub of the washer and either secure the hose with tape along the side with the end pointing up. If the appliance is a top-loader washer, stick the hose's end into the tub of the washer and lower lid on top of the hose without crushing it to secure it in place.

4. Trim removal - if painted and caulked to the wall surface, use a utility knife to cut the caulking, use a hammer and pry bar to remove the trim from the wall surface one section at a time.
5. All tiles are removed using a small bucket filled up and thrown into trash bags (ONLY filled a quarter of the way) and thrown into trash trailers and/or dumpsters.

6. Cover all furniture and personal items. If you are covering computers or electrical items, use a cloth (*never plastic*).

Dirt Removal - *Small amounts* of dirt and/or landscaping may be spread throughout the yard at the client's request in a designated area.

Foundation Terminology

Foundation – the platform in which the structure is built and supported. It can be made of concrete or raised off the ground made with a treated lumber structure supported by metal or concrete piers.

Form – the framed perimeter of the area where concrete is poured. A series of supported lumber used to hold in the concrete as it cures.

Footings – this is a deeper and wider part of the slab meant to bear the structure's weight on the corners and the perimeter walls. A foundation footing needs to be all along the perimeter anywhere the Roof's weight will be bearing down.

Vapor Barrier is a sheet of Visqueen laid down directly on leveled soil or gravel bed before concrete is poured to prevent moisture from wicking through the concrete. The moisture can disrupt the concrete's integrity over time and cause the concrete to "sweat." This is the rare instance where visqueen is used as the permanent vapor barrier in construction.

Slab - concrete base to the structure. The ground will be excavated, leveled out, and graded for proper drainage. Sometimes a gravel bed is laid down on top of the soil.

Raised Foundation - a platform built above the ground at 12" - 12' above the ground surface, depending on where you live.

Tips & Standards

1. *Concrete slabs* - the ground is graded and leveled. Any in-ground plumbing is laid down; a perimeter form is made with 2x lumber.

2. A vapor barrier (*Visqueen*) to prevent the concrete from "sweating" in humid conditions is laid down

3. *Raised floors* -the ground is to be graded to water run to run beneath the house and flow into the street or designated water runoff.

4. Concrete footings are used under the perimeter and any support wall piers

5. Termite caps on top between the pier and treated beam

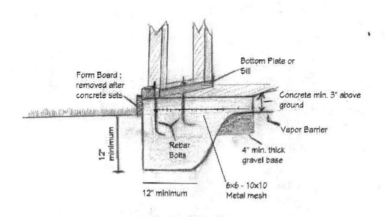

Form Board ; removed after concrete sets

Bottom Plate or Sill

Concrete min. 3" above ground

Rebar Bolts

Vapor Barrier

4" min. thick gravel base

12" minimum

12" minimum

6x6 - 10x10 Metal mesh

Raised Floor Foundtion

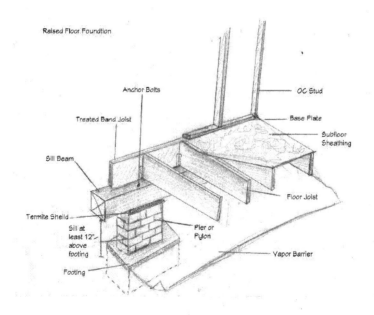

Anchor Bolts

OC Stud

Treated Band Joist

Base Plate

Subfloor Sheathing

Sill Beam

Termite Sheild

Floor Joist

Sill at least 12" above footing

Pier or Pylon

Vapor Barrier

Footing

Framing Terminology

Framing is constructing the walls, ceilings, roof, windows, and doors using precut milled lumber.

Plumb – perfectly vertical.

Level – perfectly horizontal

True - staying in as straight of a line as possible but making allowances for unevenness or imperfections. Usually used when lining up new construction with existing out of level or plumb construction

Treated Lumber – Lumber that has been chemically pressure treated exposed to moisture and weather conditions can retain structural integrity.

Non-treated Lumber – is any lumber that has not been treated and will lose all structural integrity if exposed to the weather and extreme moisture.

Structural members: is the stick lumber that makes up the walls, ceilings, roof, windows, and doors giving support in making up the structure of the building.

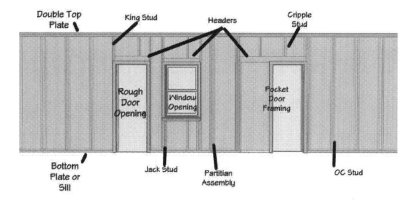

Studs - the lumber (*2x4 interior & exterior walls, 2x6 exterior walls only as a rule of thumb*) installed vertically, making up the wall from the bottom plate to top plate.

Joists - the support from wall to wall for a ceiling and/or the floor for a raised foundation.

Rafters – are the lumber that makes up the Roof. It starts at the peak of the Roof (*ridge*) to the end of the eave on top of the exterior wall plate.

Soffit – is the space between the rafter tail (*Eave*)and the wall. Use 5/8" thick Plywood, Hardi board, or vinyl to fill in this space.

Fascia – is the board along the end of the rafter tails. It can be concrete board, wood, echo board with a groove (*hardened wood through a treatment process*), or vinyl to clad the fascia.

Rough Opening – is the framed opening for doors, windows, shower pans, niches to fit the finished item. It is larger than the thing installed. The measurement is derived by adding the finished item's measurement or desired opening to the finish wall products' thickness. Either Drywall, siding, trim work, and/or tile and backer materials.

Open Walls - the stick lumber is in place, and only the exterior plywood is attached to the studs of the framework with the Rough-In Electrical, Plumbing, and HVAC lines showing.

Knee Wall – also known as a Pony Wall. It is a short wall, generally 36" – 42" in height. It is used as a partition between spaces, dining rooms, kitchens, a shower wall (*with a glass panel attached on top*), a tub wall, retaining wall, etc.

Niches – this is any recessed section of a wall. In living areas, it is used to display artwork. In Bathrooms, it is typically used in showers and near bathtubs for shampoo and soap bottles.

Black-in - the plywood is attached to the outside of the walls and Roof; house wrap is attached to the exterior walls, and roofing felt is attached to the roof plywood. It is the first layer of waterproofing.

House Wrap – is usually a plastic or synthetic barrier used to protect the plywood sheeting on the outer walls. It is located between the sheeting and the siding preventing rain from getting inside the wall.

Ceilings - the top surface of any room space separating the living area from the attic.

- *Flat* - straight across from wall to wall. Standard is 8' - 9'. New homes range from 10' - 12' high in living areas.

- *Vaulted* - raised at an angle on two sides of the room following the rafters and flat in the middle. It is not necessarily the same pitch as the Roof.

- *Cathedral* – is raised on two sides, and the room follows the rafters to the Roof (*ridge*). It is the same pitch as the Roof.

- *Shed* – the ceiling will slope one only on one side and then flatten out. It is built this way to add more height to the room.

- *Tray* - the room's center is lifted higher, and the room's perimeter is at a lower height.

- *Coffered* - the ceiling is framed out into several squares of equal size. It is built in framing or using trim work.

- *Dome* - a rounded dome is framed into the ceiling, usually is 1 section or room is a full circle

- *Barrell* – is a rounded ceiling from one wall to another that follows the length of the room.

Windows – generally installed during the house's framing phase, is appropriately sealed before the siding goes is installed. They can be installed later.

- *Sash* - the framework that holds the glass in place. There is an Upper Sash (top panel of glass) and a Lower sash (bottom panel of glass)

  - Fixed - the pane of glass does not move

  - Single-hung - the bottom sash is the only pane that moves up and down.

  - Double-hung – is the bottom and top sashes both move.

- *Hang* - indicates how many of the panes of glass are operable.

  - Single-hung - the lower half of the window lifts and lowers

  - Double-hung - both the top and bottom panes of glass lift and lower

- *Tilt* - indicates if the pane of glass will be able to tilt in for cleaning purposes.

- *Mullions* - otherwise called grids or grilles are the spacers used to break up the pane of glass. They may be internal, sandwiched between the sheets of glass, or external.

- *Sill* - the bottom frame of the window

- *Header* - the top frame of the window

- *Jamb* - the sides of the inside frame of the window

- *Channel* - the window's interior part that the lower and/or upper sash use to slide up and down.

○ *Glazing* – is the seal between the frame of the window and the glass. *Size* - usually indicated with four numbers to tell the window's width and height in that order. Ex: 3050 is 3'0" wide x 5'0" tall. Ex 2: 2648 would be 2'6" wide x 4'8" tall.

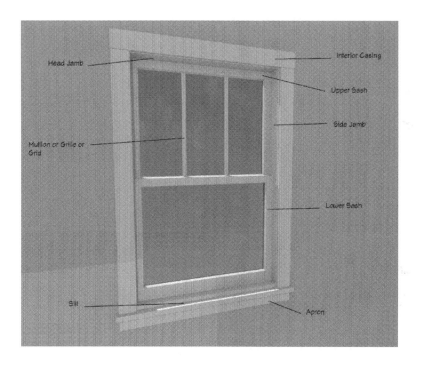

<u>Doors</u> -

- *Exterior Door* – these are the doors installed on the exterior walls of the structure. They will be exposed to weather conditions. They are hung during the framing process before the siding goes on or can be installed later. It will require more work.

- *Interior doors* – these are the doors installed only inside the structure. They will not be exposed to any weather conditions. The doors will typically be hung after the Drywall is complete and the rest of the trim work.

- *Jamb* - the sides of the door frame

- *Header* - the top of the door frame

- *Stop* - the small trim in the middle of the jamb that makes the doorstop swinging.

- *Swing* - (*Pivot*) the direction the door pivots If on hinges

  - Left hand: when standing outside the door, it will open away from you to the left.

  - Right hand: when standing on the outside of the door, it will open away from you to the right

  - Inswing: the door opens into the room or to the inside of the house

  - Outswing: the door opens to the outside of the room or the house.

- *Size* - usually indicated with four numbers to tell the door's width and height in that order. EX: 3068 is 3'0" wide x 6'8" tall

- *Sidelights* – these are the fixed panels on either side of the door that are glass with either no grills or several to break up the glass into panels. Sometimes the decorative glass is used in the sidelights.

- *Threshold **or** Transition-* is the bottom part of the frame for the door. For exterior doors, the threshold slopes away from the interior of the house. A Transition is also the change of flooring for an opening from one room to another. EX: the shift from the bathroom to the bedroom and/or hall. Thresholds and Transitions will come in many wood or metal with different colors and finishes.

- *Bore* - the hole cut in the door to fit the lockset

    - *Single Bore* – for one handle

    - *Double bore* – one for the handle and one for the deadbolt

- *Strike plate* - the plate on the closing side of the jamb that the door bolt from the lockset extends into, helping to keep the door closed.

- *Mortis* – this refers to the carved-out indent in the jamb for the hinges and the strike plates.

- *Hinges* - the pivot points fixed on the door jamb, allowing the door to pivot. Available in rounded or square edging with many options in colors and finishes.

- *Hollow-core* - a molded door that is hollow inside

- *Solid core* - the door is made of the materials all the way through.

- *Fiberglass* - no rot, fiberglass. If dented, it will not rust or rot.
- *Steel* - no rot steel, if dented, will rust.

- *Wood* - solid core wood. If it is overexposed, it will rot. Wood needs upkeep on the exterior surface.

- *Styles* are the names for the different types of doors and let you know how they function and look.

  - <u>Barn</u> door OR <u>Library</u> door – slides side to side in front of the door opening. The sliding hardware is attached above the door frame on the wall—any material and chosen design.

  - <u>Sliding</u> – either only one or both panels will slide from one side to the other. It may be used for exterior and interior applications.

  - <u>Pocket</u> - door slides back into the wall. A particular frame is used during the framing process to accept the door. It has a track at the top for the door to slide open and closed.

  - <u>Bifold</u> - the door is in 2 sections that "fold" out to the side. Closets

  - <u>Double </u>door - 2 doors that open in the middle and swing open to the outside.

  - <u>French</u> doors - exterior doors (*typically*) that both swing out simultaneously with no center style.

  - <u>Patio</u> doors are the exterior doors with one side fixed (*non-opening*), and one side swings open.

  - <u>Pivot</u> – standard door that swings open and hinged to one side.

  - <u>Café Doors </u>– these are doors that swing in both directions.

Standard Door Frame

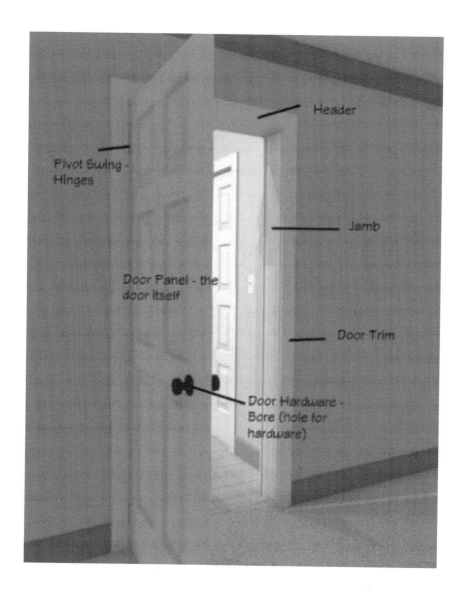

Header

Pivot Swing - Hinges

Jamb

Door Panel - the door itself

Door Trim

Door Hardware - Bore (hole for hardware)

Tips & Standards

1. House wrap is to be attached using button cap nails or staples. Standard covers all of the walls, including doors and windows, and cut back at the windows and doors, leaving a 4"-5" overlap (*fold to the inside*) of the doors and window jambs using a utility knife.

2. *Windows* – to frame a window is having a header: 2x6 on top of the window supported by 2x4 Jack studs which run on either side of the window opening and King Studs are attached to the Jack studs from floor to ceiling.

3. *Ceilings* - joists may be installed 16" - 24" apart on center. The following are recommended sizes according to the open ceiling span (*the width of the room*)

   16" OC 2x4 - 9' or less   24" OC 2x4 – 7' or less
          2x6 - 13 feet or less   2x6 – 10'6" or less
          2x8 - 16 feet or less   2x8 – 13' or less
          2x10 - 19 feet or less   2x10 – 16' or less
      * LVL (laminated beams) are usually recommended for spans 20 feet or more

4. Rafters - are spaced usually 16" to 24" apart on center. The following are recommended sizes according to the rafter lengths needed from ridge to eave:

   16" OC 2x6 - 12 feet or less 24" OC 2x6 – 11 feet or less
          2x8 - 17 feet or less   2x8 – 14' 10" or less
          2x10 - 20 feet or less   2x10 – 16'6" or less
   2x12 - 24 feet or less   2x12 – 19' 6" or less

5. *Awnings* - are framed 6" - 8" on either side of a door and/or window. The awning will cover at least 3' in front of the door or window to properly shed water away.

6. *Broken seals* – to tell if the seals on windows have broken after a storm, place a piece of ice on the surface of the

window.   If condensation appears between the panes of glass, the seal is compromised.

Standard Roof Framing

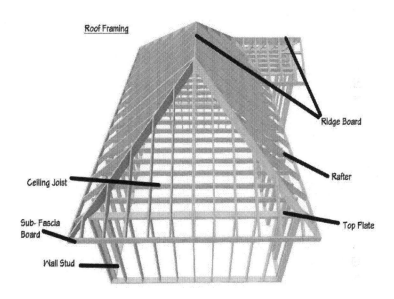

Roofing Terminology

Roofs - the angled structure that protects the house from weather and temperature changes

Valley – is the mitered corner where two roof planes meet at the bottom.

Ridge – is the top or Apex of the Roof, where all the rafters connect on both sides.

Pitch - denotes the amount of slope the roof has. The higher the pitch, the steeper the slope. The number indicates how many inches of the rise there is for every 12 inches of length. Example: 3 on 12 pitch (*written 3:12*) rises 3 inches for every 12 inches of horizontal length.

Eave – the overhang of the Roof from the external walls of the structure.

Underlayment - the roofing felt (*3' wide rolls*) attached to the decking using button cap nails. It is laid horizontally from the eave to the ridge.

Shingles - the asphalt materials attached to the roofing felt on the Roof made in 2'x3' sheets laid horizontally starting from the bottom edge (*eave*) in a staggard pattern to the top (ridge)

- 3-tab shingles - a single layer of granular materials on a fiberglass matt base. Used on roof pitches of 2:12 and higher

- Architectural - multi-layer shingle made with fiberglass, organic materials, and asphalt. A heavier matt base than the 3-tab shingle. Used on roof pitches of 3:12 or higher. These shingles help the watershed on high pitch roofs.

- Luxury shingles - multi-layer shingle made with fiberglass and asphalt. They are made to imitate cedar shingles. Lots of dimensions. Helps the watershed on high pitch roofs

- <u>Cedar shakes</u> - individual cuts of wood made from cedar. Used on roofs with a 4:12 pitch or higher. HIGH maintenance.

Metal - sheets of metal about 16" wide and cut to the desired length to cover the Roof. Some metal roofs require a purlin strip to be attached to the Roof first before connecting the metal.

- <u>Purlin strip</u> – is a 1" x 1" strip of treated wood, cut to the desired length between the underlayment and the metal.

- <u>Corrugated</u> - the metal is wavy and is attached using screws with rubber gaskets. The screws and gasket are exposed to the elements and will degrade over time, causing leaks.

- <u>Standing seam</u> – is the metal sheets are flat for about 12" then have a small ridge; this pattern is repeated throughout the roof slope. The sheets are attached with screws with rubber gaskets where each sheet overlaps the next, concealing the screws. It has a much longer life and far fewer leaking than a corrugated roof.

Penetrations – anything protruding from the Roof on its normal sloping plane.

o *Roof jack*s - pipes that come out the top of the Roof. They are the extension of the plumbing vents stacks for your bathroom, laundry, and kitchen drains required.

o *Vent hood cap*s – is the cap for the vent hood in the kitchen.

o *Fireplaces* - most true brick fireplaces are built separate from the house framing and have an independent footing. They will need to have proper flashing to help the water and ice move off the Roof and not leak down the chimney's sides.

o *Skylights* – these a large square or rectangular window put into the Roof.

- Solar tubes - a small tube that is capped with a plastic dome to let light into the space like a skylight, but with less risk of leaking

- Dormers – are a structure protruding vertically from the main Roof of the house. They will be roofed to match the house and usually have a window. It allows for more headspace in a 2nd story room and/or attic. They can be part of the home's original construction or added later, varying in sizes and styles depending on the home's architecture.

Roof Styles

- <u>Flat</u> is the Roof slope only up to 10 degrees, just enough to have water move to the Roof ends.

- <u>Gable</u> – double-pitched roof on two sides of the roof, and the building's end wall goes up to and follows the roof lines to the ridge.

- <u>Hip</u> – multiple sloped Roof; sloping on all roof planes, if the whole Roof is hipped, then all sloping sides intersect at the ridge.

- <u>Gambrel</u> - "barn" part gable roof but will have multiple pitches from the ridge to the eave (*soffit*), leaving the end wall to go up to the ridge peak.

- <u>Lean-to OR Shed</u> – is the single pitch roof that will slope in one direction from top to bottom. They are used on sheds, awnings, additions, and patios.

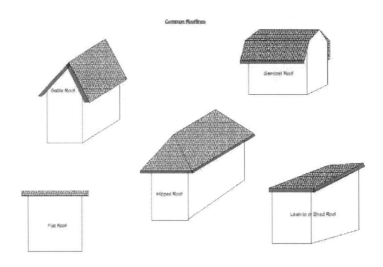

Common Rooflines

Tips & Standards

Items to look for to know if you are having issues with your Roof:

o   Shiny Shingles – all the grit has been lost due to erosion. And you are looking at the raw layer of the shingle.
o   Fish Mouth – the middle of the shingle is popping up and looks like a fish's open mouth.
o   Missing or broken shingles
o   Adhesion Breakdown – the shingle releases easily when pulled on. It makes the roof vulnerable to leaking. Shingles are made to stick together to form a "solid surface" on your Roof.
o   Cracking due to nail pops.

Roof Layers

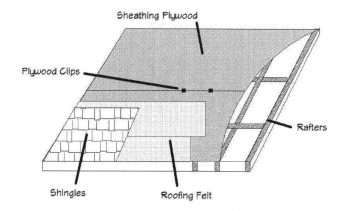

Siding Terminology

Siding - the outer cladding of a structure. The façade or facing of the building. The following are the most used siding materials.

- **Concrete Board** – are concrete boards attached with screws or nails made for the concrete boards.

  - *Lap* - the boards are cut in 4" - 12" widths and come in 10' or 12' lengths. The boards are attached, lapping one over the other, starting at the bottom of the wall to the top. The seams are staggard along the way. Will have either a smooth or woodgrain texture.

  - *Panel* - a sheet of concrete board in 4'x8' - 4'x 10' sizes. It will have a smooth, woodgrain, or stucco texture. They are attached vertically butted up to each other. The seams are caulked, and/or trim is placed over them.

  - *Board & Batten* – panel board, hung vertically with 1x2 strips of lattice trim of wood or concrete board pieces to cover the seams. Trim pieces are placed over seams every 4' apart and every 12" – 24" in between the 4' panels to add decoration.

  - *Shaker* - 2' x 3' sheets molded to look like shaker wood pieces. Attached with screws or nails and lapped over one another from the bottom of the wall to the top.

  - *Trim* - 4" - 8" wide, 10' - 12' lengths, ½" – 5/4" thick boards used to border the top, bottom, and corners of walls, doors, and windows as well. It comes in either smooth or woodgrain texture.

- <u>Wood</u> - exterior cladding made of wood

    - *Lap* - wood cut into 4" - 12" wide boards at 10' -12' in length. Each board laps the previous board starting from the bottom of the wall to the soffit

    - *Panel* - 4'x8' and 4'x10' plywood sheets attached to the house wrap. The seams are then covered with a trim, caulked, and painted.

    - *Shaker* - small rounded off pieces of wood butted against each other on the horizontal and lapping over each other on the vertical starting from the bottom of the wall to the soffit.

- <u>Brick</u> - masonry human-made product attached to the exterior house wrap using brick ties and mortar: heat, moisture, and temperature resistant.

- <u>Stucco</u> - a mortar type product applied on concrete board and used in a 3-layer part system consisting of a scratch coat 3/8" thick, a brown coat 3/8" thick, and a finish coat 1/8" thick. Usually, a concrete board is installed under the scratch coat. A colorant may be applied to the topcoat before it goes on or painted after it is applied.

- <u>Vinyl</u> - a plastic human-made sheet designed to imitate lap siding, installed to protect the house's outside walls from rain and sun exposure. Available in many different designs and colors.

- <u>Concrete</u> – solid concrete walls. Either they are made from solid concrete formed and put together or from cinder blocks filled with concrete after formed.

- <u>Log</u> – precut logs notched and stacked one on top of the other.

- <u>Shaker</u> – 4" – 8" pieces of individual pieces of wood staggered in a row and lapped one on top of each other. Stamped concrete boards are available in the shaker look.

Tips & Standards

1. When installing any cut ends of wood siding, prime all edges that may come into contact with water, primarily the bottom two rows of lap siding.

2. To install any siding, make sure to mark a level line at the bottom of the wall before installation.

3. To install vinyl or lap siding, use a siding gauge installation tool that allows you to space the boards' layers properly.

4. Any bubbling effects in the vinyl siding can indicate moisture issues.

HVAC Terminology

HVAC Terminology - Heating, Ventilation, and Air Conditioning

Full unit – is one unit calculated to condition the air for a space of varying sizes to condition the amount of space in the home. The entire unit is composed of many parts. The main components are the Condenser, Compressor, and the Air Handler.

Condenser - (*outside unit*) Air conditioner condensers are a heat exchanger device. The Condenser rejects heat from the air conditioner system to surrounding air. While the evaporator absorbs heat from the space that needs to be cool. In our case, it is from indoor air.

Compressor - (*outside unit*) An air conditioning compressor is the part of the air conditioning system that compresses cold, low-pressure gas into a hot, high-pressure gas. The compression of this gas helps keep the area cool.

Air Handler - (*in the wall or attic space*) moves the air from the return across an air conditioner's evaporator coil, also called the evaporator core. That is where the cold air is produced. The evaporator coil is located inside or near the air handler where the blower fan is that blows the conditioned air out of the registers.

Trunk lines – (*ductwork*) are the tubes running from the central unit to the registers in the attic and between floors.

Registers - the holes cut in the ceiling, floor, or wall and covered with a metal multi-directional vent to allow the cooled or heated air into the room

Air Return – the wall-mounted vent inside the home where the air is taken in for circulation. It is where you can locate your filter.

Mini-split is somewhat of a hybrid of a window unit and a full unit for heating and cooling areas and allows you to control the temperatures in individual rooms or spaces. Mini-split systems have two main components - an outdoor compressor/condenser unit and an indoor air-handling unit (*evaporator*).

Window - a small unit placed in a window to heat and cool a small space. Always check the box recommendations for the square footage you want to cover

Tips & Standards

1. Pour 1 cup of bleach in your AC condensation relief pipe to clean out the built-up of deposits once a month.

2. Change out your AC filters once a month

3. Make sure of the type of filter your system needs. When in doubt, use the cheapest filter you can buy. If you buy a filter made with multiple filters, it can be too thick and not allow for proper airflow. It will put a strain on your system and can cause it to freeze up.

4. Keep vegetation away from you outside the condenser unit.

Insulation Terminology

Insulation - the materials to help protect the interior space from outside elements of moisture and temperature; also, a material used to wrap electrical wires to prevent the current from being passed to and through other materials. Used in between walls, floors, in attic spaces or attic ceiling, under sub-floors, around windows and doors, wrap plumbing pipes, and water heaters.

- Roll batten - fiberglass packed and different densities for different protection levels with a thick paper backing install in between exterior wall studs and ceiling joists (*attic side*). Attached with staples if there is a paper backing or simply cut and place to the desired length if there is no paper backing.

- Blown-in –tiny fiberglass bits of insulation in different densities for different protection levels that are blown into the spaces between wall studs and ceiling joists. If being used in between wall studs, first, a mesh is stapled to the studs, cut back around outlets, and a hose is inserted at the top of the wall while the insulation fills the space using a machine. Blocks of insulation are fed into the machine, broken up, and blown through a large tube.

- Foam - a liquid foam that expands and hardens once it hits the air. It comes in different densities for different levels of protection.

  - Open-cell - soft foam that is sprayed in a thin layer and quickly fills up with tiny air holes to expand p to 10 times its original size

  - Closed-cell – is more rigid foam with tiny air holes to none, allowing no air to pass through. It is usually metal buildings and roofs.

- Sheet - a sheet of Styrofoam 1/4" - 1" thick. It can be cut to the desired size and offered in various densities for different levels of protection.

Zone	2x4 walls	2x6 walls	Attic	Floors	Crawlspaces
7	R13 – R15	R19 – R21	R49 – R60	R25 – R30	R25 – R30
6	R13 – R15	R19 – R21	R49 – R60	R25 – R30	R25 – R30
5	R13 – R15	R19 – R21	R49 – R60	R25 – R30	R25 – R30
4	R13 – R15	R19 – R21	R49 – R60	R25 – R30	R25 – R30
3	R13 – R15	R19 – R21	R49 – R60	R25	R19 – R25
2	R13 – R15	R19 – R21	R30 – R49	R13	R13 – R19
1	R13 – R15	R19 – R21	R30 – R49	R13	R13

Plumbing Terminology

Plumbing – is the system of pipes, tanks, fittings, and other apparatus required for the water supply, heating, and sanitation in a building.

Rough-in – is the series of piping, tanks, and connections under the structure, allowing for drainage and supply lines to all necessary valves sets.

P-trap - a U-shaped pipe that holds water preventing odorous sewer gases from rising into the house. Regular use of the water line is required to make sure water stays in the trap's bottom. If the house is not in use for any reason, flush toilets and run faucets at least once a month. They are on every tub, sink, shower, and tub in the house.

Finish - the "pretty" Fixture attached to the end of the supply or drain lines. Sinks, sink fixtures, toilets, tubs, shower, and tub fixtures, etc.

Cleanouts – is a capped pipe attached to the sewer line to allow for cleaning out the debris. Found on the outside of the house along the line that leads out to the main public sewer line.

Water heater – is the tank of water that heats the water for all fixtures in the house.

Fixtures (*faucets*) - the finished valves for showers, tub, sinks

Valve Set – is the piece of the water supply line where the flow of water is turned on and shut off. It will also mix the hot and cold-water lines coming to the supply line.

Drain – the pint at which the water leaves the building through a series of pipes to the main drainage line

Toilets – is the seated Fixture mounted to the wall or wall to remove body waste from the home.

Shower Fixtures – valve sets and spouts used inside the shower area

Tubs Fixture– any valve set and spouts used for Tubs

Sink Faucets – the valve set and spout used for a sink typically centered between the wall and sink edge

Shower Pans- is the bottom flooring of the shower. It is made from a solid surface, or a pan is made and then finished with a tile.

Curbs – the Transition from the interior of the shower to the outside of the shower

Tubs – is for soaking and bathing while sitting down or reclining. The typical size is 60 "long x 15" high x 30 "– 32" deep. There are many more sizes available. Be sure to check with your Vendor if a larger tub is preferred.

- o *Apron* – will fit in between 2 walls or cabinets and have a molded front

- o *Decking* – the top rim of the tub usually 2" – 3" wide. It can be either molded with the tub or built around any tub and surfaced with any water-resistant materials. (*usually, tile or solid surface material is used on the countertops.*) if the decking is built around a tub, it is usually 12" wide or more, depending on the preference.

- o *Overflow* – is the built-in "drain" for any tub toward the top rim of the tub. It is built in to help drain the tub if it is filled too high.

- o *Drop-in* – will have a deck built around it and "dropped" into the decking with the top flange overlay on top.

- Garden tub – a large soaking tub that can be jetted or non-jetted. It can be a drop-in or an apron tub

- Freestanding – the tub will stand alone away from the wall with all sides exposed.

  - Clawfoot – will have feet at the bottom of the tub
  - Pedestal – sits on top of a solid base

Sinks - bowls that hold water for kitchens, bathrooms, outdoor kitchens, laundry rooms. Variety of sizes, shapes, materials, and colors. Typical Bath vanity size is 16" – 20" side x 5" deep. Standard dimensions for a Kitchen sink are 30" – 36" wide by 8" – 12" deep.

Styles
- Drop-in – is the bowl that mounted on top of the countertop.

- Undermount - mounted under the countertop with silicone and flanges. Used only on solid surface countertops

- Vessel bowl – is a single basin sink that sits on top of the countertop.

- Pedestal – single basin sink attached to the wall with a column type base

- Wall-mounted – is a single basin sink attached to the wall. The drain and supply lines are exposed.

- Apron – (farm sink) large Basin with a front that comes down the front of the cabinet

- Single Basin - no division inside the sink

- ○ *Double Basin* – having two wells inside the sink for water

  - 70/30 - divided into 70% and 30% of the sink
  - 60/40 - divided into 60% and 40% of the sink

- ○ *Bar* - smaller single basin used on a bar for rinsing – 12" -18" wide.

- ○ *Utility/laundry* - large deep single basin used to soak clothes and sheets.

Materials

- *Stainless Steel – (most used)* a family of iron alloys that contain Chromium composition that helps prevent the rusting of the iron elements. It may also have other metals such as nickel and Molybdenum to help prevent corrosion and increase integrity. The lower the gauge of stainless steel, such as 18 gauge, the better quality the steel.

    - *Applications: under-mount, drop-in, apron*

- Porcelain – is a cast from china clay and a silicate material into a solid form. It is then coated with a hard-shell glaze to prevent moisture from getting into the porcelain. It ships easily when heavy pots are dropped on it and can scratch over time.

    - *Applications: drop-in and apron*

- Quartz – cast from a quartzite, sand, and colorant mixture to form a solid sink. Non-porous and hard to scratch.

    - Applications: under-mount, drop-in, apron

- Stone – natural stone formed and honed into a solid sink. Non-porous and durable. May scratch easily.

- Copper – can be either pure copper or mixed with other elements to offer a long-lasting finish and resistance to rust and/or corrosion. It may scratch easily.

Tips & Standards

1. Pour vinegar and/or bleach into the disposal while running a least once a month to clean out any debris and build up.

2. Clean the faucet heads with vinegar and/or bleach once a month to remove any surface mildew and /or build-up.

3. Clean out any shower and sink drains once a month to remove hair and soap build-up.

Electrical Terminology

Electrical – is the power supply for any structure.

2. <u>Panel</u> - An electrical panel is also called a *load center*. It is a metal electrical service box that accepts the home's main power and distributes electrical current to the house's various circuits.

3. <u>Gang</u> – is the box inside the wall-mounted to the stud that houses the wires for the switches and outlets, available in 2" deep to shallow boxes of 1" and ½" deep.

    o *Single gang* - holds one switch or outlet

    o *Double gang* - contains two switches or outlets

    o *Triple gang* - contains three switches or outlets

    o *Four gang* - hold four switches or outlets.

    o *Pancake* - shallow (1/2" deep), different sizes, round metal or plastic "box" used to hold the wires for lighting fixtures in either the ceiling or the wall for sconces.

4. <u>Circuits</u> – are located inside the panel, having a dedicated area of the home wired directly into it. Each circuit has a shut off individually for work in an area. If there is an overload of power to that circuit, it will shut off automatically to prevent arching and possible fire.

5. <u>Junction boxes</u> are where all the wires from different rooms are joined in one location and connected to the primary panel.

6. <u>Conduit</u> - the plastic or metal piping used to house electrical wire for protection and acts as a safety barrier.

7. <u>Rough-in Electrical</u> -the installation of panels, circuits, wires, junction boxes, conduits, and gang boxes, outlets, and switches

8. <u>Finish Electrical</u> – is the installation of the light fixtures, fans, outlet and switch cover plates, appliances. They should be tested with light bulbs when installed.

9. <u>Outlet</u> - power source where outside appliances large to small are plugged

   o *Duplex* - standard outlet with three-prong input available for both inputs.

   o *GFCI* - (*Ground Fault Circuit Interrupter*) outlet with a shut-off and reset capability usually installed in all wet areas of the house, kitchens, baths, and outdoor kitchens. Usually, only 1 GFCI is required in each area.

   o *Appliance* - each appliance, refrigerators, dryers, etc. will sometimes require a specific outlet type. Be sure to look up the Owner's Manual for your model to make sure you purchase the right cord and the correct outlet installed.

10. <u>Switches</u> - manually operated circuit breaker to turn on lights and /or outlets

    o *Single pole* - operates only one Fixture

    o *Three-way* - gives the ability to turn on and off lights from 2 different places, but controlling only one light or a set of lights (*recessed or pendant*)

    o *Four-way* - gives the ability to turn on and off lights from 3 different locations, but only controlling one light or a set of lights (*recessed or pendant*)

- ○ *Dimmer* - gives the ability to control the amount of light coming from the light fixture from dim to bright.

- ○ *Three function* - (*Multi-function*) used to control a fixture. Example: Heater, Vent, Lights for bathrooms.

11. Lighting

- ○ *Recessed lights* - mounted inside the ceiling to be flush with the surface of the ceiling. It consists of a housing (*in the ceiling or attic space*), a light kit (*inside the housing*), and a beauty ring (*trim kit on the outside flush to the ceiling*), which can be painted to match the ceiling.

- ○ *Flush mount lights* - mounted to the ceiling or wall without hanging from a down rod or chain.

- ○ *Pendant lights* – are hanging lights from the ceiling with a down rod or a chain.

- ○ *Wall-mounted* - mounted to the wall.

  - • Vanity lights - lights made to hang over the bathroom sink area.

  - • Sconce lights - smaller lights usually in hallways and/or on either side of the mirrors for and vanity mirror or an art piece. A patio will also have sconce lighting.

- ○ *Security* – is bright lighting outside the house, with either a motion detector, direct switch, or both to light up an area at night to deter trespassers.

- ○ *Utility* - bright lighting in areas that require a lot of light to work. Kitchens, workshops, sheds, laundry rooms, etc.

- ○ *Soffit* - small 4" recessed lights in the soffit to light up the exterior of a house

- ○ *Undermount* - mounted under cabinets and/or shelves to give light to countertops. May be switched to a dedicated dimmer switch if hardwired into the wall.

- ○ *Landscape* – solar or hardwired lights in steps, posts, along pathways, gardens, trees, or specific areas.

Tips & Standards

1. Once the finish fixtures are installed, they are tested by being turned on and inspected for proper working order.

2. When adding more electrical items for an addition or an outdoor patio, always have an electrician check your electrical supply box to let you know if you have a circuit available to handle the electrical amount you will be adding.

3.

4. When doing electrical work, it is essential always to use non-conducting tools, no loose clothing or jewelry that may get caught on wires or equipment.

5. When switching out outlets, fans, light fixtures, etc. it is essential to shut off the electrical supply to the area you are working in to avoid any shock.

6. Recessed Canned lighting – is used for a utility purpose and task lighting. It needs to be placed not to cast shadows, and if place around a fan, use four cans surrounding the fan in a living area if multiple fans are set (*outdoor space*) rule of thumb is four can lights for every fan to avoid a strobe effect.

7. Electricity is not slow. If it takes a while for the light to come on, there is something wrong with Fixture's circuit.

8. When plugging in appliances to an outlet, it slides in and out easily; it may be time to change your outlets.

Drywall Terminology

Drywall Sheets -boards made from a mixture of plaster, wood pulp, and/or other materials used on the interior facing the walls and ceilings of a home or other structure.

Standard Drywall - inside the home, standard drywall sheets are installed. It offers insulation and a small sound barrier. The most common sizes are ½" and ¼." ½" is generally used in new construction.

Seams - where two sheets of drywall meet. Should be butted up against each other.

Tape – is a paper or fiber strip used to cover the Drywall's seam to give it a smooth appearance and seal the Drywall once the mud is applied.

Mud - the joint compound used to attach the tape to the Drywall and smooth out seams of the Drywall to prep it for paint and /or wallpaper. It is to give texture to a wall or ceiling surface.

Floating – is the mud used to smooth out seams and screw head and/or any small blemishes in the Drywall. Standard floating will require more than one coat or "pass." Each pass is floated, sanded, and then floated again and sanded again. With each sanding, a finer grit of sandpaper is to get a smoother finish. After floating is complete, the walls should have the 1st coat of primer to show any blemishes in the mudding, and additional floating may be done before painting if necessary.

- *Wallpaper* - may only require one pass if floated correctly and smooth after sanding so that no bumps or bubbling occurs under wallpaper.

Skim - a light coat of mud to get rid of roughness or texture.

Texturing is an application of drywall mud on the Drywall's entire surface to hide flaws or as part of the Design (*usually on ceilings*).

Patching - any blemishes or holes in Drywall, having the damaged Drywall replaced, taped, and floated. The Drywall will be cut back to the nearest stud, fastened to the stud (*to make sure it does not bow out from the wall or ceiling*).

Abatement – is the removal of the top layer surface material. If a wall or ceiling is not the desired texture, it can be removed and smoothed out. In the Drywall Standards, this is usually referred to when discussing Popcorn ceilings. The popcorn texture can be abated, and a smooth surface applied.

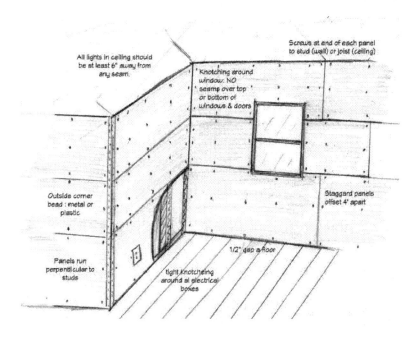

Tips & Standards

1. Hang the sheets factory edge to factory edge and cut edge to cut edge.

2. Walls are hung horizontally to reduce the span of seams in larger spaces.

3. No seams are to be above doors and windows; they could eventually crack due to the doors and windows opening and closing.

4. Each end of the Drywall must be screwed into the lumber structure member.

5. When cutting back damaged Drywall, cut back the Drywall to halfway or just past the nearest "clean" stud. It allows you to attach the new piece with the edges that are secured to the structural lumber.

6. Screws should sink just below the surface of the Drywall, not too deep or sticking out. If it is too deep, it could crack the Drywall, and if the screws stick out, it will not be smooth when the mud is applied.

Painting & Staining Terminology

Painting – is the color coating on the wall, ceiling, trim, doors, and windows.

- *Prime coat* - Sealer put on the wall and ceiling to help the paint adhere to the surface.

    - Base: If using acrylic on Drywall paint, use an acrylic primer. When using oil-based paint for trim, use an oil-based primer. DO NOT use an oil base on top of a water-based; it will bubble and need to be sanded and recoated.

    - Color: if covering a dark color with light color paint, use a grey primer (*tinted light or dark*). If covering and light color with a light color or dark color, use a white primer

- Base Coat - the first coat of paint applied to the wall or ceiling

- Topcoat - the final coat of paint

- Sheens - the amount of shine the paint finish will have

    - *Flat* - no shine at all, hard to clean any smudges to marks

    - *Eggshell* - very low shine, easy to clean

    - *Satin* - very low shine, easy to clean

    - *Semi-gloss* - somewhat of a shine

    - *Gloss* - very high shine, easy to clean

- <u>Base</u> – is the makeup of the paint.
  - Acrylic- is a water-base, not as hard of a shell in the final coat.
  - Oil - oil-based, having a hard shell when cured after seven days.

- <u>Faux Finish</u> – is the painting technique used to create a desired finish to the surface—for example: to mimic stone, simple glazing, or to "age" wood. It usually requires a trained Tradesman and several layers of paint and top coating.

- <u>Clear-Coat</u> – apply a clear sealer, allowing the surface color to come through. It will darken the color slightly. Sealers come in different sheens of flat to glossy.

- <u>Saturation</u> – is the depth of color in the paint.

- <u>Flashing</u> – the noticeable difference in the sheen in a spot usually when a touch up is in higher sheens of Finish. The higher the gloss, the more prominent the flashing will be. The entire area will have to be repainted to make the flashing disappear.

- <u>Holidays</u> – are an area where the paint did not take to the primer. The primer coat will be slightly visible through the 1st coat of paint. It can occur because of many reasons, so an additional coat of paint will remedy the holidays.

Choosing the Right Sheens & Bases		
Sheen	**Area**	**Base**
Flat	Ceilings	Latex
Eggshell	Walls: *Bed, Bath, Kitchen, Living, Dining, Laundry & Hallways*	Latex
Satin	Walls: *Bed, Bath, Kitchen, Living, Dining, Laundry & Hallways*	Latex
Semi-Gloss	Trim Work, Doors, Windows, Cabinetry	Oil-Based
Glossy	Rarely used: furniture for the lacquered look	Oil-Based

Staining Terminology - a colorant added to the wood surface to either change the wood's natural color or enhance the wood's natural color. A topcoat or Sealer will typically be applied to protect and seal the wood. It is NOT necessary in all cases to apply a sealer when used for an interior application in a conditioned area.

Tips & Standards

1. The Drywall is then coated with one coat of primer to see if any floating defects need to be corrected. If there are defects, sand the area and repeat the same floating process as before

2. All trim (*crown, baseboards, shoe molding, door and window trim, wainscoting, all casings, and cabinetry*) need to have the nail holes filled with paintable putty, and all the seams are caulked with paintable caulk.

3. Sometimes caulk will shrink if it dries too fast (*in lower temperatures and arid climates, i.e., the AC could be set too low*), and the second pass of caulk will be necessary.

4. Protection - any surface you wish NOT to get paint on (cabinets, countertops, appliances, windows, floors, furniture) is covered in brown paper and/or plastic visqueen and secured with painters' tape on all edges. Painters tape is NOT left on all for an extended period.

5. When painting your walls and trim, your lightest color (wall or trim) paint the lighter color first. Then paint your darkest color next (wall or trim). It is easier to paint over the lighter color when cutting in than the darker color.

Trim and/or Finish Carpentry Terminology

Trim and Finish Carpentry – is the finishing carpentry touches of any construction job.
- <u>Trim</u> is installing any moldings for walls, ceilings, doors, windows, cabinets, stairs, flooring, etc.

  - *Crown* - the molding used to trim the wall to ceiling. Many different styles and sizes. It can be painted or stained.

  - *Step Crown* – uses multiple moldings to create a large molding with a look and style. Many different styles and sizes are applied in steps or layers. May be painted or stained.

  - Transitions – the molding installed between 2 different types of flooring or where the flooring changes direction. It Is generally at a doorway or wall opening.

  - *Baseboard* - the molding used to trim out the wall to the floor. Many different styles and sizes. May be painted or stained.

  - *Shoe* - the molding used to trim out the baseboard to the flooring. Many different styles and sizes either shoe base (*it is taller than it is wide at its base*) or ¾ round (*3/4 of a full circle in shape*). May be painted or stained.

  - *Casings* -molding used around openings between rooms. Many different styles and sizes. May be painted or stained.

  - *Paneled* - the molding used to divide up a wall or section of a wall or ceiling into Square or rectangular sections. A single molding used, or multiple moldings may give different looks and style, depending on the desired effect.

- ○ *Door* - the molding on two sides and top of the door frame on both sides to the door. Many different styles and sizes. May be painted or stained.

- ○ *Window* - the molding on both sides, top, and bottom of the window. The window may have a sill (*a flat "shelf"*) at the bottom and the **apron** molding under the sill. It can also have no sill, and the molding will look more like a picture framing. Many different styles and sizes. May be painted or stained.

- Wainscoting - paneling applied to the wall at about anywhere from 36" - 60" from the ground. Standard is at about 36" at finished height. Paneling is used below the chair railing trim to the baseboard.

- Chair railing – the top trim applied above the Wainscotting paneling to give a finished look.

- Bath accessories - wall mounted hooks and hangers to hold bathroom essentials—a wide variety of styles and finishes.

  - ○ Toilet paper hanger - should be near the toilet, either wall-mounted or a freestanding stand.

  - ○ Towel bars - available in many sizes and finishes to hang drying towels.

  - ○ Towel rings - used for hand towels near sinks. Available in many styles and finishes.

  - ○ Towel warmers - wall-mounted near the tub and/or shower. Available with temperature controls and timers.

- Towel racks - freestanding or wall-mounted to hang drying towels.

  - Robe hooks - available in many styles and finishes.

- Shower doors - glass doors that open and close to keep water in the shower. Available in many sizes and finishes. Standard dimensions may be ordered and installed with a 1" - 2" variance. Other showers will need to be measured (*template*) and made especially for the space. It will take anywhere from 2-4 weeks, sometimes longer depending on the Design.

  - Pivot - the door will swing on hinges

  - By-pass - both panels of glass move side to side

  - Sliding - one fixed panel and one moving panel (*side to side*)

  - Framed – is the shower door, and any panels are framed out with metal will include headers and thresholds.

  - Frameless - no framework around the glass except the hinges and wall brackets and any support headers.

- Shower rods - used to hold curtains and liners. Available in many sizes and finishes.

  - Adjustable - a tension rod that will adjust to the space provided

  - Fixed - screwed into the wall as a permanent fixture

  - Curved - rod is curved outward to allow more space for the liner and curtain, either adjustable or fixed.

- Mirrors - many shapes, sizes, and finishes. The vanity mirror size will depend on the height of the vanity light and the sink faucet. For vanities, the most common types of vanity mirrors are fixed, hanging, and medicine cabinets. Medicine cabinets can either be recessed or flush mounted to the wall.

- Hardware - handles on doors and drawers for opening and closing. Available in many sizes and finishes

- Countertops - the finished top of the kitchen and bathroom, base cabinets. Many different materials and colors.

  - Laminate – is a laminated product made in sheets adhered with a heavy-duty glue to a base usually made of plywood.

  - Granite - solid natural stone surface, honed to shine or a leathered finish and many different colors.

  - Marble - solid natural stone surface, honed to a shine.

  - Tile – the tile of choice adhered to a concrete board surface.

- Backsplashes are surface material mounted to the wall between the countertop and the bottom of the upper cabinet or just above the countertop in the baths and kitchens.

Tips & Standards

1. If you have a textured surface on the ceiling, the crown will have small gapping where you have the texture surface variation.

2. When measuring along the wall, measure drywall surface to drywall surface or outside of the corner if turning on a wall.

3. When fitting the trim together, you will need a tiny gap. It allows the wood to expand and contract throughout the hot and cold temperatures and the different humidity levels that occur year-round.

4. Install baseboard at least 1/4" from the floor surface. If the floor is uneven, install the top of the baseboard level, leaving the uneven gapping between the bottom of the board and the floor. Make sure the widest gap between the board and the floor is NO more than a 1/4". It will ensure the coverage by the shoe molding.

5. If you are NOT using a shoe molding, then the baseboard will have to be installed AFTER the flooring is installed. It will "sit" flush on top of the flooring.

6. If the Inside corners are TOO TIGHT, this will result in the baseboards bowing out away from the wall, causing gaps

7. Install shoe molding snug against floor surface and baseboard.

Tile & Stonework Terminology

Tile Work – is the installation of any tile on walls and floors. Tile is made of many different substances such as porcelain, ceramic, glass, metal, natural stones (*marble, travertine, granite, etc.*), terra cotta, slate, brick. The average thickness of a tile is 3/8" thick. It can run up to ½" thick depending on the size and material. Tiles are cut into specific shapes and sizes and for different applications. (*discussed below*) All tile needs a sub-structure to attach. For example, a structural wall with waterproofing backer materials, concrete, or raised flooring structure is prepared to accept the tile.

Stonework – is the application of brick, stones, and large pavers to walls and floors. The brick and/or stone is used in creating walls and floors (*usually exterior applications*), whereas tile needs to have a sub-structure to attach. Brick and stone will be of varying sizes and thicknesses.

Tile Backer Materials - these are the materials used to adhere tile to and ensure waterproofing behind the tile.

> Hardi backer boards: this is a concrete board attached to the studs around the shower and overlaps the shower pan or tub flange lip using screws designed for the Hardi backer board.

> Schluter systems: shower pans and a plastic Ditra (*a thin orange sheet hung using mortar*), shower benches, and niche inserts. Ditra needs to be applied with a thin-set (*the mortar*) and allowed to dry.

> Red Guard / Hydro ban: a liquid vinyl rolled over the Hardi backer board, Ditra, and shower pan to prevent leaks. It is rolled on thick with no gaps or open spots. It must be allowed to dry overnight before tiling

> Laticrete hydro board: moldable shower pans, wallboards, benches. It is screwed to the studs or

Drywall using screws designed for the Laticrete hydro board.

Laticrete sealant: a caulk like a Sealer to run along the seams and all screw heads of the hydro boards. Once the sealant is applied, it is ready to start setting the tiles. There are no wait times for drying.

Thin-set: this is the concrete mix designed especially for tile setting. There are different types for different applications and vary in drying times. It is widely used because it is heat and moisture resistant and can be used to level out uneven areas. It is usually left to dry overnight before grouting.

> A white, modified thin-set is always used with glass tiles.
>
> Modified thin-set - has an additive the strengthen the bond of the tile to the wall and/or floor.
>
> Non- modified thin-set - has no additive and generally used in drier areas.

Thin-set is generally laid about 3/8" thick. Each tile setter will have preferences, and each floor will require its type of setting depending on the floor level.

Tile Materials - tiles are made in a variety of materials and sizes. Each material has a different porosity and is used for various applications.

> Marble - very porous and soft. This natural stone is cut and honed (*polished*) to varying degrees of shine or leathered texture on the surface. The more honing a stone receives, the harder the surface becomes, making it less likely to stain. Marble has a Medium color variation with a softer "veining" throughout the stone.

Application – is usually used on a backsplash, shower walls, floors, and a room's main flooring. If the stone has a gloss, it is not ideal for a shower floor to be walked on while wet and soapy. If the Finish of the stone is NOT honed to a high gloss and has a texture, used on the shower floor. The most common application is as a countertop. It will scratch and be susceptible to heat exposure damaging the top surface requiring re-honing of the surface like a countertop. Typically used in wet areas, but not in high heat areas.

Slate - a natural stone that is made by layers of stone stacked and pressed together. It has a high color variation and is a softer stone. Highly susceptible to chipping and cracking when exposed to temperature variations, heavy traffic, or hit.

Application - used on Interior/ Exterior main flooring in living areas, patios, walkways, and paths. If using for an interior project, the slate will need sealing and resealing every 1-2 years, depending on floor use. It may be used in high heat areas and not typically used in wet locations unless sealed.

Terra Cotta – is very porous but hard. It is a reddish-orange substrate with a glazed color or painted decorative surface. Highly susceptible to chipping and cracking when exposed to temperature variations. It may be used in high heat areas and not typically used in wet areas.

Application – is used on floors in kitchens, bathrooms, living areas, patios, walkways, and backsplashes for kitchen and bathroom vanities.

<u>Travertine</u> - natural stone, very porous and soft. Medium variation color. Highly susceptible to chipping and cracking. It may be used in high heat areas and not typically used in wet areas because of porous.

> *Application* - floors in living areas, kitchen, backsplashes, and patios. Backsplashes for kitchen and bathrooms.

<u>Brick Paver</u> - human-made product, porous and very hard. Either cut from whole bricks or made to mimic bricks. Highly susceptible to chipping and cracking. It may be used in high heat areas and not typically used in wet areas because of being so porous.

> *Application* – used on walls, backsplashes, flooring in living areas, laundry & bathrooms. It is an uneven surface and will need sealing for interior applications. Sealing will need to be done every 8-10 years or if yellowing takes place. It may be used in outdoor patios, walkways, NOT used in showers since it is so porous and needs so much upkeep with sealing.

<u>Ceramic</u> – is dense and hard. Most ceramics are glazed with a color and/or decorative pattern. Highly susceptible to chipping and cracking. It may be used in high heat areas and typically used in wet areas as well.

> *Application* - typically used in flooring for living areas, bedrooms, laundry, and bathrooms. May be used for shower walls, vanity, and kitchen backsplashes if sealed.

Porcelain – is very dense and hard. This human-made material is made as a through-body color, meaning if the tile is ever chipped, the color below is the same as the surface and does not change its integrity. Some porcelain tiles colors are only on the surface as an inkjet image. If the tile chips in any way, it will show greatly but does not interfere with the tile's integrity. Not very susceptible to chipping or cracking. High variation in color and surface texture. They are used in WET areas mostly. It is used in high heat areas as well.

> *Application* – used in living areas, kitchen, bathrooms, shower walls, backsplashes, outdoor patios, walkways, countertops.

Glass - human-made, very hard, and dense. Least porous, and usually higher price points.
The backing of the glass tile may be painted, or the glass itself will be colored. Not very susceptible to chipping or cracking. High color and texture variation.

> Applications – are typically used as wall tiles in showers or backsplashes.

Recycled Glass – the glass is melted, molded, and colored to mimic other materials such as marble. It has a texture that is not slick. It is often molded into small mosaic tiles but cut into larger sizes.

Tile Sizes-

Large - 24" x 48"/ 12" x 24"/ 4" x 48" plank or 36" plank/ 4" x 10"

Application - floors and some walls

<u>Square</u> – 36"x36" / 32" x 32", 24" x 24" / 20" x 20" / 18" x 18"/ 16" x 16"/ 12"x 12" / 6" x 6"/ 4" x 4"

Applications - floors, walls, and some backsplashes

<u>Mosaic</u> – 3" x 3" / 2" x 2" / 1" x 1" / ½" x ½" or any combination of these sizes.

Shower wall accent, shower niches (shampoo boxes), shower floors, backsplashes

Tile Styles

<u>Chevron</u> - patterned where two tiles come to a point in a repeated pattern. Large to mosaic.

Applications - walls, backsplashes, floors, shower walls, shower niches (*shampoo boxes*)

<u>Penny</u> - small ½" – 1" round tiles (*approximately the size of a penny or a nickel*)

Applications - shower walls, shower floors, backsplashes, and main flooring

<u>Picket </u>- the straight thin tile with points at both ends (*to mimic a picket fence*). Large to mosaic.

Applications – used on walls, shower walls, niches (*shampoo boxes*), backsplashes.

<u>Subway</u> - 3" x 6" tile either a flat surface or beveled. Most people refer to rectangular tiles as subway tiles, but a true subway tile is a 3"x 6" tile.

Applications – used on shower walls, niched (*shampoo boxes*), backsplashes.

Tile Bullnose is the same tile you are using for the field except that one end has been rounded off and polished. Not all tiles have a bullnose option. You will need to check with the Vendor to make sure that it does. These tiles will come in a different size than the field tiles (usually 3x12 or 3x6, sometimes 2x12 or 2x6); they will be considerably more expensive than the field tile and will have to be ordered NOT by the square footage, but by the exact number you will need for edging.

Tile Pencil trim. It is a decorative tile that has a finished edge. Not all tiles are offered with a pencil trim. You may pick a specific trim that is not in the "family " of the field tile but coordinates with it. These tiles will come in a different size than the field tiles (*usually 1x12 or 1x6, sometimes ½x12 or ½x6*), they will be considerably more expensive than the field tile and will have to be ordered NOT be the square footage, but by the exact number, you will need for edging.

Grouts - grouts are offered in a large variety of colors made of cement, mortar, and colorant. Once the tile is selected, the grout should be chosen at that time.

Tile Patterns - all tile may be laid in different patterns. The most common are as follows

> Straight - all seams line up straight
> Staggard - the seams are staggard either every other tile or every 3rd tile.
> Chevron - tiles are on a diagonal with every other row going the opposite direction as the row next to it.
> Diagonal - the seams are laid on the diagonal to the room layout

Tips & Standards

1. Quality Checkpoints: Tile should be laid level and even. You should run a roll of tape over them, and it does not catch on edges or corners. The exception to this is the tiles that have a distinct texture to them, making them uneven.

2. Grout should cover the spaces in between the tiles but do not over the tiles. If the tiles have a texture, the grout may seem to "sink" below the tile's surface. All surfaces are to be left clean of any grout.

3. Thin-set is used to fill in small dips in the concrete foundation.

4. Large dips in the foundation may require a concrete self-leveling.

5. If a separate sealer is required, it must be reapplied every year. The sealers are for the grout lines and the tiles as well. It will need a new application yearly or depending on the amount of foot traffic the floor receives. If used on the wall, the application time may be every 2-5 years, depending on the use and cleaners used on the tile.

Flooring Terminology

Wood

○ *Real wood* - milled to the desired thickness and width in many different species of wood.

○ *Engineered* – is layered wood compressed in the desired thickness and width. The top layer is solid wood, and the lower layers of a composite of different woods layered in different directions giving the board strength. It resists warping.

○ *Laminate* - a synthetic product laminated together is a desired thickness and width colored and patterned to mimic real wood. It resists warping and scratching.

  ▪ Application

    ● *Glue down* - glued straight to concrete or sub-flooring of plywood

    ● *Nail down* - nailed to a subflooring of plywood

    ● *Floating* - clicked together with tabs on the planks' sides to create a solid floor that does not adhere to the concrete or subfloor. Padding is typically under this flooring. The padding can be a sound-absorbing, cushion, and/or water-resistant.

Vinyl – is synthetic plastic sheets and or tiles in different styles, textures, and colors.

- *Sheet* - cut to length and comes in 12' and 15' widths. Can be glued down or applied as a floating floo.r

- *Plank* - cut into planks in 4' and 3' lengths and 4" - 6" wide planks available in glue-down or click-lock floating applications.

- *Tiles* - cut into 12" x 12", 12" x 24" tiles that will glue down

Concrete - smoothed out a slab that can be either sealed in its natural color, stained, and/ or painted and then sealed.

Epoxy - a specific surface coating that can be colored or have colored flakes added to the mixture that will seal the concrete. Moisture resistant, chemical resistant, and stain-resistant.

Paver - bricks cut into thin tiles to be applied like tiles with mortar for adhesion and grout.

Carpet - tightly woven threads in many colors, textures, and materials; 12' and 15' widths cut to desired lengths.

Tile Work – is the installation of any tile on walls and floors. Tile is made of many different substances such as porcelain, ceramic, glass, metal, natural stones (*marble, travertine, granite, etc.*), terra cotta, slate, brick. The average thickness of a tile is 3/8" thick. It can run up to ½" thick depending on the size and material. Tiles are cut into specific shapes and sizes and are for different applications. (*discussed below*) All tile needs a sub-structure to attach. Example: a structural wall with waterproofing backer materials; a concrete board or raised flooring structure prepared to accept the tile

Tips & Standards

1. Most flooring installed is at least ¼" away from the wall, especially wood and laminate flooring. It will allow for expansion and contraction of the flooring.

2. Shoe molding is generally on most flooring except carpet.

3. Always order 10% more than your actual square footage needed. It will help to account for the cut off and /or waste when cutting the floor to install.

4. Thresholds will be used as a break for wood and laminate flooring so it does not buckle. Thresholds are also used between different types of flooring.

Cabinetry Terminology

Cabinetry

- <u>Base</u> – is the lower cabinets attached to the wall
  .

- <u>Upper</u> – is the wall cabinets attached to the wall above the base cabinets.

- <u>Island</u> - freestanding base cabinets in not attached to any walls

- <u>Peninsula</u> – is a freestanding base cabinet attached on one side only to perimeter wall cabinets.

- <u>Pantry</u> - a full height unit from floor to ceiling with either pull out shelves, drawers, or adjustable shelves.

- <u>Full</u> - the same as a pantry unit with different purpose storage

- <u>Shelves</u> - inside the cabinet to stack items

  - Roll out - having slides allowing it to be pulled out and pushed into the cabinet. Will have small sides so that items do not fall off while in motion.

  - *Fixed* - the shelf permanently set into the cabinet.

  - *Adjustable* - holes cut into the side of the cabinet interior and shelf pins placed into the holes allowing the shelf to be placed in any setting and moved later.

- <u>Shelf pins</u> - pins that slide into the holes on the side of the cabinet and hold the shelf in place

- <u>Hinges</u> - allows the door to swing open and closed.

  - *Self-closing* - at a certain point in the pivot of the door, the hinges will pull the door closed

  - *Soft closing* - at a certain point in the pivot, the hinge will offer a slight resistance to close the door gently without slamming

  - *Standard* - allows the door to pivot with no resistance.

- <u>Bumpers</u> – clear plastic bumpers stuck to the back of drawers or doors so they do not slam against the cabinet's face frame.

- <u>Slides</u> are the drawer's mechanism, allowing it to slide open and return into the cabinet.

  Self-closing - at a certain point in the drawer's return into the cabinet, the slides will pause the closure and pull the drawer entirely into the cabinet softly.

  Soft closing - at a certain point of the closure of the drawers, the slide will offer resistance and close softly with no slamming.

  Standard - opens and closes the drawers with no resistance. It allows the drawer front's slamming, which can damage the cabinet's drawer front or face.

- <u>Hardware</u> - the pulls or knobs used to open and close the doors and drawers

    - *Pulls* – are handles in various lengths: 3", 5", 7", 10" and up with two screw holes.

- *Knobs* - a round or square piece. One screw hole.

- <u>Frameless</u> - the cabinet box will have no face frame showing because the doors and drawer fronts will cover the entire face frame.

- <u>Framed</u> - the cabinet front will have a face frame made of stiles and rails for the doors and drawer fronts to rest on; it will show. (*traditional*)

- <u>Face frame</u> - the front of the cabinet that shows behind the doors and drawer fronts with cutouts for doors and drawers.

- <u>Stile</u> - the vertical part of the face frame

- <u>Railing</u> - the horizontal part of the face frame

- <u>Overlay</u> - the doors and drawer fronts rest on the face frame.

- <u>Full Overlay</u> - the doors and drawer front will cover the face frame

- <u>Inset</u> - the doors and drawer fronts are flush inside the face frame

Tips & Standards

1. Base Cabinets for a Kitchen, usually is 36" high x 22" deep are standard. The length will be decided by space available and customer preference.

2. Upper cabinets are mounted to the wall anywhere between 15" - 20" above the base cabinets' top. The standard height placement is 18" above the countertop.

3. Island is a finished cabinet on all sides, standing independent, not attached to any wall. All islands are required to now have electrical outlets if they are fixed to the floor.

4. The vent pipe needs to vent through the roof and vent out on top of the Roof and weather cap installed.

Countertops Terminology & Standards

Countertops

Fabricators –the Vendors with the equipment to cut the solid surface slab to fit the countertops to include the cutouts for appliances, sinks, and the polished edging. Most of the fabricators will also sell solid surface material (*natural stones, Quartz, Silestone, etc.*)

Wholesalers – These vendors sell the slabs of stone. They do not fabricate the stone. You will have to find a fabricator of your own. They will, however, deliver the slab to the fabricators for you.

Solid surface is a slab of solid material, either human-made or natural stone. 2 cm - 3cm in thickness. It is rated in Tiers 1-3, Exotic.

> *Tier* 1 - speckling in color
> *Tier* 2 - less speckling and some veining
> *Tier* 3 - more veining with slight speckling
> *Exotic,* mostly veining. Not as commonly found as the tier 1 - 3 stones

Materials -

> Granite: natural slab from a quarry. Wide range of colors and styles. Very dense moisture, heat, and light-resistant to changing the integrity of the stone. They are used for interior and exterior uses.

> Soapstone – is a natural stone form quarry. NO speckling. Wide range of colors and styles. It is a soft stone that is susceptible to showing scratches. It is moisture, heat, and light-resistant to changing the integrity of the stone. They are used for interior uses.

Marble: natural slab from a quarry. NO speckling. Wide range of colors and styles. It is a soft stone that is susceptible to showing scratches. It is moisture, heat, and light-resistant to changing the integrity of the stone. They are used for interior and exterior uses.

Dolomite - a mix of granite and marble. Natural slab from a quarry in a variety of colors and styles.

Quartz & Silestone - human-made slab manufactured to imitate stones. It is EXTREMELY dense will not scratch or crack easily. Completely moisture resistant and heat resistant. However, repeated exposure to heat daily in the same spot will, over time, change the stone's color to a yellowish color in that spot. It will yellow in direct sunlight outside every day. They are not used for exterior uses. HONED Finish only.

Finishes

Honed - polished to a shine and slick surface. It creates a seal for the stone.

Leathered - the honing is not as deep and leaves the surface with a slightly bumpy surface and matte Finish. It feels like a piece of leather. It will give the same stone a difference in color.

Matte – homed to a smooth surface that is not shiny at all.

Edging – are the edges of the countertop that can be finished in many ways. The customer will choose their preference. The following are the most common types.

Bullnose - rounded over

Eased - the corners are softened by remains "squared."

Beveled – is an angle cut to the edge then straight down.

Ogee - curved cut put into the edge

Chiseled - rough cut and jagged, unpolished

Wood - painted or stained with MULTIPLE coats of the clear coat or wax applied Finish.

Concrete - formed up and concrete poured, sanded down, and refinished multiple times to achieve a smooth surface.

Laminate - a human-made sheet in varying colors and styles applied to a plywood base with glue—moisture resistant. Do NOT put hot pans and pots on the surface; it will cause the laminate to separate from the plywood base and bubble and eventually crack. If moisture gets through the crack, it will delaminate the plywood base.

Backsplashes - this is covering on the wall between the countertop and the underside of the wall cabinet. The backsplash may go from the top of the countertop to the ceiling or the ceiling trim to create a more dramatic effect. Backsplashes are a place to get creative. It can become a feature or blend into the background, depending on the desired result.

Tips & Standards

1. Backsplashes are installed after the countertops.

2. Always purchase 10% more backsplash tiles than the exact square footage.

3. The countertop will be the complement to your cabinets in your kitchen and bathroom.

4. Having large "pot drawers" on your base cabinets helps prevent getting on the ground to reach the cabinet's back to locate an item.

5. Lazy Susan in corners will take up a lot of space because of the circular shape inside the base or upper cabinet box. It should also have a tall lip to the spinning shelf to prevent an item from falling off while turning the shelf and getting lost in the cabinet's back.

The Value of Your Project

It will depend on what you want to get out of your Project as to how much you want to put into it. Here we will discuss the difference between your Project being your Forever Home or an Investment Property that you either resale or rent out.

1. **Forever Home** – this is the home you do not plan to move out of until you either go to the nursing home or die! The materials you use in this home will typically be items you will want to last a long time and be of the highest quality. They will improve your lifestyle quality as you live in the home and give you the most pleasure. The items you will spend the most money on will be:

    a. Countertops
    b. Plumbing faucets
    c. Light fixtures
    d. Doors & windows
    e. Flooring
    f. Tiled showers
    g. Glass for shower doors
    h. Appliances
    i. Roofing
    j. Hardware

2. **Investment (Flip House) Or Rental -** this is a house you may see as an opportunity to update the inside and outside then sell for a profit. These can be tricky to invest in, but it can be worth your time and investment with the right preparation. The property could have also been an inheritance that you may need to sell. You will want quality products, but on a mid-level budget to increase the possible profit. Keep your colors and choice of fixtures as neutral and mainstream as possible to appeal to a larger pool of buyers. The areas to concentrate on are:

   a. **Kitchens –**

      i. <u>Countertops</u>: Tier 1 granite with a subway tile backsplash. A timeless look at a modest cost.

      ii. <u>Cabinets:</u> consider painting existing cabinets a white or soft grey to remain neutral but have a fresh look.

      iii. <u>New hardware</u> – stainless steel or satin nickel will have a neutral effect but a fresh look.

   b. **Bathrooms –**
      i. <u>Shower/Tub walls:</u> subway tiles shower walls. At least one bath (usually the hall bath) with a tub.

      ii. <u>Countertops:</u> Tier 1 granite with matching 6" backsplash

      iii. <u>Sinks:</u> oval white under-mount; this is a clean and fresh look

      iv. <u>Faucets:</u> stain nickel single handle

c. **Flooring:** install a "wood" laminate, vinyl click lock, or porcelain tile throughout the house. Neutral in coloring. Carpet only in the bedrooms if at all.

NOTE: For rental properties, you will need to replace items regularly, so consider using durable products. It will apply to the flooring, especially.

Made in the USA
Las Vegas, NV
05 March 2022

45071287R00063